ROBERT SCHUMANN

QUINTET

for Piano, 2 Violins, Viola
and Violoncello
E♭ major/Es-Dur/Mi♭ majeur
Op. 44

Ernst Eulenburg Ltd
London · Mainz · Madrid · New York · Paris · Prague · Tokyo · Toronto · Zürich

CONTENTS

Ernst Eulenburg Ltd
48 Great Marlborough Street
London W1F 7BB

PREFACE

The early 1840s were one of the happiest periods of Schumann's life. After many difficulties and much unpleasantness he had at long last married Clara Wieck, and for the first time his success in the symphonic field was undeniable. Also his connection with Mendelssohn and other leading musicians of his time, as well as the *Zeitschrift für Musik*, which he had founded himself, had won him overall recognition and respect. All these outer circumstances stimulated his creative genius, and for the first time he turned his attention to chamber music. The first compositions of the productive year 1842 were the three String Quartets Op. 41, which were to remain the only string quartets Schumann ever wrote. Immediately afterwards he set to work on the combination of pianoforte and string quartet, a combination which up to that time had been completely unknown. It is amazing that this undoubtedly daring experiment led to a masterpiece that earned Schumann fame and popularity as only few of his other compositions did. Almost all later composers of chamber music (Brahms, Franck, Dvořák, Reger, etc.) imitated Schumann's Op. 44 and made use of the same instrumentation.

The Piano Quintet was completed in October 1842, and received its first performance in Schumann's house in November, with Clara Schumann at the piano and the Gewandhaus Quartet under the direction of Ferdinand David. Another performance took place at another private house on 8th December. As Clara Schumann fell ill shortly before that date, Mendelssohn took her place and played the difficult work at sight. On his advice Schumann replaced the original middle section (in A flat) of the second movement by the present F minor episode, and also composed the second Trio of the Scherzo (which, in the MS, is only found in the appendix). The first public performance took place in the Gewandhaus on 8th January 1843, this time again with Clara. The success was such that the work had to be repeated on 9th February. The very same year it was published by Breitkopf & Härtel.

Max Alberti

VORWORT

Die frühen 1840er Jahre waren besonders glücklich in Schumanns Leben. Nach langen Schwierigkeiten und Kämpfen hatte er seine Braut Clara Wieck heimführen können, und ihm war zum ersten Mal unbestrittener Erfolg auf symphonischem Gebiet beschieden. Zudem war er durch seine Verbindung mit Mendelssohn und anderen führenden Musikern sowie durch die von ihm gegründete *Zeitschrift für Musik* zu allgemein anerkanntem Ansehen gelangt. Diese Umstände bestärkten ihn in seiner Schaffenskraft; erstmalig widmete er sich der Kammermusik. Das erste Erzeugnis des fruchtbaren Jahres 1842 waren die 3 Streichquartette Op. 41, die die einzigen von Schumann bleiben sollten. Unmittelbar darauf machte er sich an die bis dahin noch nicht dagewesene Zusammenstellung von Klavier und Streichquartett. Es ist erstaunlich, dass gerade dieser zweifellos gewagte Versuch zu einem Spitzenwerk geführt hat, das ihm wie wenige andere seiner Schöpfungen Ruhm und Popularität einbrachten. Dieselbe Besetzung ist daraufhin von fast allen späteren Komponisten von Kammermusik nachgeahmt worden: Brahms, Franck, Dvořák, Reger usw.

Schumann beendete sein Quintett im Oktober 1842, und im November wurde es erstmals von Clara Schumann und dem damaligen Gewandhaus-Quartett unter Leitung von Ferdinand David in seinem Hause gespielt. Eine weitere Aufführung fand am 8. Dezember in einem anderen Privathaus statt; da Clara kurz zuvor krank wurde, sprang Mendelssohn ein und spielte das schwierige Werk vom Blatt. Auf seinen Rat ersetzte Schumann einen ursprünglichen Zwischensatz in As im 2. Satz durch den jetzt vorhandenen in f-Moll. Ebenso verdankt das zweite Trio zum Scherzo seine Entstehung dieser Anregung (es ist im Manuskript nur im Anhang vorhanden). Die erste öffentliche Aufführung fand, wiederum mit Clara Schumann, am 8. Januar 1843 im Leipziger Gewandhaus statt und hatte solche Wirkung, dass das Werk bereits am 9. Februar wiederholt wurde. Noch im gleichen Jahre wurde es vom Verlag Breitkopf & Härtel verlegt.

Max Alberti

PIANO QUINTET

Robert Schumann
1810–1856
Op. 44

I

p
cresc.
p
cresc.
cresc.
cresc.
cresc.
20
f
f
f
f
f
p

30

p

p

p espress.

p

p

40

cresc.

f

f

cresc.

f

cresc.

f

cresc.

f

50
p
p
p
p
dolce
poco ritard.
a tempo
dim.
mf
p

60

espress.

mf

70

un poco rit.

p dim.

p

p

cresc.

dim.

a tempo

dim.

dim.

p

p

dolce

80
p
espress.
p
mf
mf
p
cresc.
cresc.
cresc.
90
cresc.

un poco ritard.
100
a tempo con fuoco
p
sf
f
cresc.
110

1.
2.
1.
2.
120
sfp
sfp
dim.
sf

180
cresc.
f
cresc.
dim.
p non legato
p

140

poco a poco cresc.

poco a poco cresc.

poco a poco cresc.

poco a poco cresc.

poco a poco cresc.

150

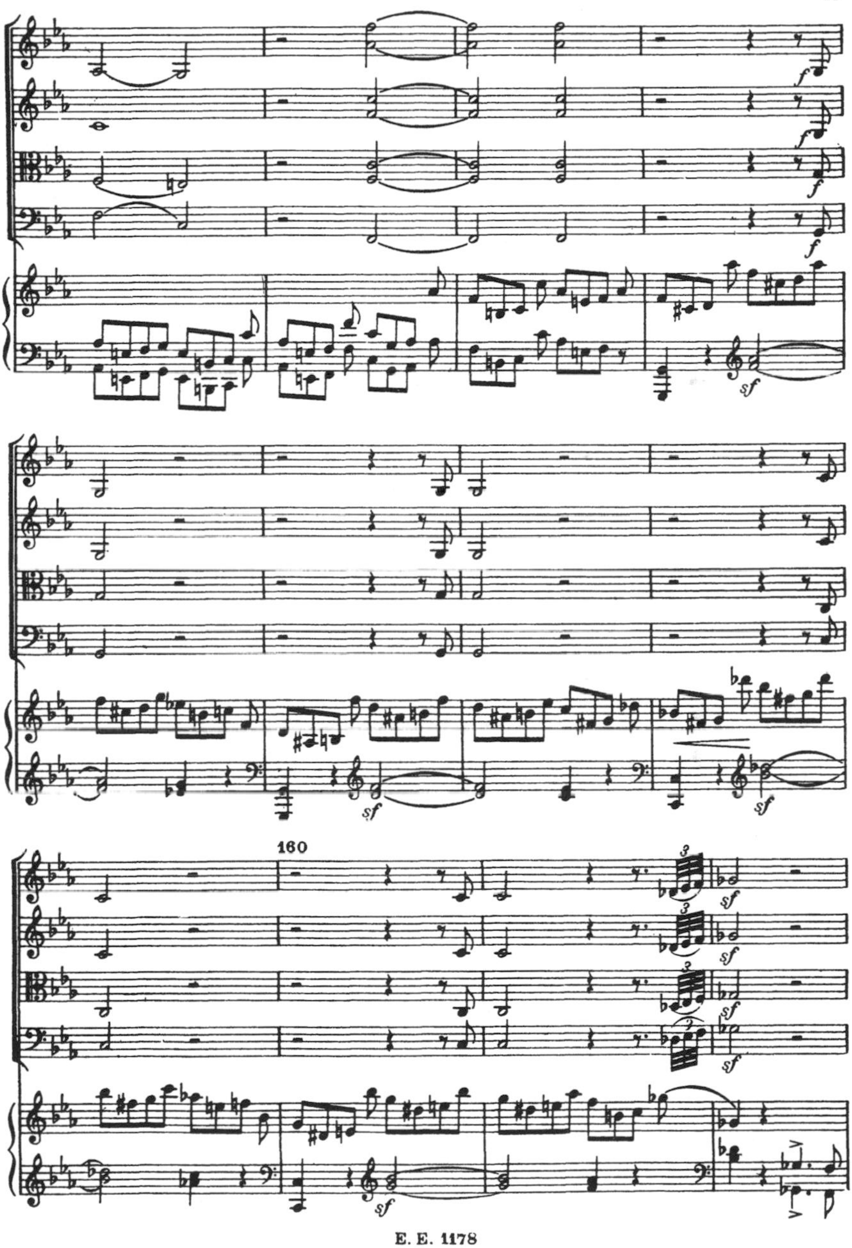

160

180

p *p* *p*

p *p* *p* *p*

cresc. *cresc.* *cresc.* *cresc.* *cresc.*

E. E. 1178

riten.
molto cresc.
molto cresc.
molto cresc.
molto cresc.
sf
molto cresc.
sf
a tempo
210
ff
ff
ff
ff
ff
Più tranquillo.
fp
fp
fp
fp
fp

220
p
p
sf
p cresc.
cresc.
cresc.
cresc.
f
f
f
f
sf
f
230

p
p
p
240
p espress.
p
p
cresc.
cresc.
cresc.
cresc.
cresc.

250
f
f
f
f
f
p
p
p
p dolce

260
un poco ritard.
a tempo
dim.
f espress.
mf espress
270
un poco rit.
p
dim.
p
p
dim.
p
cresc.
dim.

a tempo
280
p
p
p
p
p dolce
espress.
p
mf espress.
p
290
cresc.
cresc.
cresc.
cresc.

poco rit.
300
a tempo
cresc.
p
dolce
poco rit.
a tempo
p
sf
f
cresc.
310
con fuoco

f

f

f

f

820

330
8

II

In modo d'una Marcia. 𝅗𝅥 = 66. Un poco largamente.
Violino I
Violino II
Viola
Violoncello
Pianoforte
molto p ma marcato
p
p
p
10
p
p

20
dim.
marc.
pp
1.
2.
pizz.
arco
30
espress. ma sempre p
sempre p e legato

pp
p
40

pp pp pp pp più f più f più f più f

50

60
1.
2.
pp
p
70

dim.
dim.
marc.
dim.

80

pp
pp
pp
pp
pp

ritard.

pizz.
dim.
pizz.
dim.
dim.
dim. pizz.
dim.
dim.

arco
90
arco
arco

E. E. 1178

Agitato.
f
f
f
f
sf
sempre f
sf
3
sf
sf
sf
sf
sf
sf
sf
sf
sf
sf
sf
sf
sf
sf
100
sf
sf
sf
sf
sf
sf
sf

sf
ff
1.

2.
110
p
f
marc.
p
2.
sfp
cresc.

120
sf
sf
sf
marc.
sf

130
dim.
ritard.
dim.
dim.
sf
dim.
a tempo
p espress.
p espress.
p espress.
p espress.
sempre legato e p

140

pp
pp
pp
pp
150
più f
più f
più f
più f
più f
cresc.

160

ritard.
a tempo
pp
p
pizz.
170
arco

180
pizz.
dim.
dim.
arco
pp
dim.
dim.
arco
pp
arco
f
pp
pp
190
p
p
arco
pp
pp
pp
pp
pp

III

Scherzo molto vivace. ♩. = 138.

20
sf
p
30
cresc.
f

ten.
f
ten.
f
f
ten.
f
ten.
f
ten.
ten.
f
f
f
ten.
40
f
f
f
sf
sf
sf
sf
sf
sf

Trio I.

p
dim.
pp
70
1.

2.
ten.
80
cresc.
cresc.
ten.
cresc.
f
ten.
cresc.
f
ten.
2.
ten.
cresc.
f
ten.
ten.
f
f
ten.
f
ten.
f
ten.
ten.
ten.
ten.
f
f
ten.
ten.
ten.
90
f
f
ten.
ten.
f
f

 E.E. 1178

sf
sf
sf
sf
100
sf
sf
p
p
p
p
p

110
cresc.
ten.
f
120
sf

Trio II.

L'istesso tempo.

f
ff
140
pizz.
sfp

pizz.
p
sfp
150
arco

160
cresc.
cresc.
f
f
f
cresc.
f
f
sf
sf
pizz.
sf
sfp

170
pizz.
p
sfp
f
180
arco
sf
ff

ten.
ten.
200
marc.
ten.
ten.
ten.
marc.
ten.
ten.
ten.
marc.
ten.
ten.
ten.
ten.
ten.
ten.
ten.
ten.
ten.
ten.
ten.
ten.
ten.
210
sf

f
p
sf
p
sf
p
p
sf
p
220
cresc.
ten.
230
f
cresc.
ten.
f
cresc.
f
cresc.
ten.
f
cresc.
f
ten.

ten.

f

ten.

f

f

f

ten.

sf

sf

Coda 240

sf

sf

f

sf

sf

ff

sf

con brio

sf

sf

sf

sf

sf

sf

f

sf

sf

sf

sf

marcato

250
sf
p
cresc.
molto cresc.
8
260
f
ff

IV

Allegro, ma non troppo. 𝅗𝅥 = 126.
Violino I
Violino II
Viola
Violoncello
Pianoforte
sf
f
sempre marcato
10
ff

20

sempre f

30

f

sf

f

f

sf

sf
sf
40
sf
p
sf
sf
p
p
sf
p
pizz.
arco
pizz.
arco
pizz.
arco
pizz.
arco

pizz.
50
arco
pizz.
arco
pizz.
arco
p
pizz.
p
marc.
cresc.
cresc.
f
cresc.
arco
p
cresc.
f
cresc.
f
60
f

p
mf
70
cresc.
f
8

80

f *f* *f* *f*

poco dim. *poco dim.* *poco dim.* *poco dim.*

f

poco dim.

p

pp

90

pp *p espress.*

pp *p* *pp* *p* *pp* *p*

pp

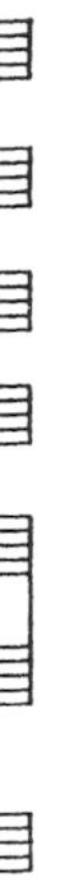

100
f marc.
p
p
p
cresc.
pp
pp
110
pp
p dolce
pp
pp
marc.
pizz.
p
arco
p
p
p

120
p
marc.
cresc.
cresc.
130

sempre cresc.
sempre cresc.
sempre cresc.
sempre cresc.
sempre cresc.
ff
ff
ff
ff
sf
sf
ff
ff
sf
140
sf

sf *sf* *sf* *sf*

sempre f

170
f
sf
sf
sf
sf
180
pizz.
pizz.
pizz.
pizz.
p
p
p
p
p

arco
pizz.
cresc.
arco
pizz.
cresc.
arco
pizz.
cresc.
arco
pizz.
arco
cresc.
cresc.
legato
arco
p
190
cresc.
arco
cresc.
cresc.
arco
cresc.
cresc.
f
f
f
f
f

200
p
p
p
cresc.
cresc.
cresc.
cresc.
cresc.
210
8
f
f
f
f
f
8

pizz.
dim.
f
dim.
dim.
pizz.
dim.
8
f
dim.

220
arco
ff
ff
ff
arco
ff
ff
p
p
p
p
p
con

230
cresc.
cresc.
cresc.
cresc.
anima
cresc.

p
cresc.
240
f

250
p
cresc.
p cresc.
260
f

270
dolce

280
cresc.
cresc.
cresc.
cresc.
cresc.
3
cresc.
cresc.
cresc.
f
f
f
f
sf
sf
f
290
p
p
sf
sf
sf
sf
sf
sf
p
p
p

cresc.
cresc.
cresc.
cresc.
cresc.
800
ff
sf
ff
ff
ff
marcato
ff
sf
sf
sf
sf
sf
sf
sf
sf
sf
sf
sf
sf
sf
sf

310
sf
ritard.
320
a tempo
sempre f
330
sf
sempre f

sf
sf
sf
sf
sempre f
sf
sf
340
ff
sf
sf
sf
sf
sf
sempre f
sf
sf
sf
350
sf
sf
sf

sf
sf
sf
sf
sempre marcato
360
sf
sf
sf
sf
sf
sf
sf
sf
sf
sf
370
sf
sf
sf
sf
sf
sf
sf

un poco rit.
a tempo
sf
p
380
cresc.
390
cresc.

400
f
sempre f
ff sempre

sf